THIS BOOK BELONGS TO:

NAME	
ADDRESS	
PHONE #	
EMAIL	

DEDICATION

This Home Maintenance Log Book is dedicated to first-time and seasoned homeowners who want to track and record house repairs and monthly tasks for home projects.

You are my inspiration for producing this book and I'm honored to be a part of your record-keeping and organization.

HOW TO USE THIS BOOK

This Home Maintenance Log Book will help you by accurately planning, recording, and organizing your information.

Here are examples of information for you to fill in and write the details of your logbook.

Fill in the following information:

1. Home Maintenance Monthly Schedule - Use the checklist to schedule routine maintenance such as furnace and AC care, appliance inspection, clean and inspect outdoor areas of the home.
2. Maintenance Contact Information - Keep track of repairmen by documenting company name, phone number, and email address.
3. Monthly Maintenance Log - Record appliance serviced, date, repair cost company, date completed.
4. Project Planner - Record project, description, material list, expected cost, actual cost, completion date, total budget, professional service used, and total cost.
5. Home Improvement Planner - Record project, date, budget, materials, timeline, steps/to do, notes, and resources.
6. Household Manufactures - Record product name, manufacturer, brand/model, contact information.
7. Warranty Log - Record item, purchase date, manufacture name, cost, expiration date, warranty contact information.

HOME MAINTENANCE SCHEDULE

JANUARY
○ Clean Drains
○ Clean and Chalk Showers and Sinks
○ Change Furnace Filter
○ Vacuum Refrigerator Coils
○
○
○
○
○

FEBRUARY
○ Clean Garbage Disposal
○ Test Carbon Monoxide and Smoke Detectors
○ Clean Range, Hood, Filters and Fans
○ Touch Up and Repaint Indoor Rooms
○
○
○
○
○

MARCH
○ Inspect Fire Extinguishers
○ Inspect Roof for Winter Damage
○ Clean Gutters and Downspouts
○ Check Chimney
○
○
○
○
○

APRIL
○ Power Wash Siding
○ Clean Out Window Wells Of Debris
○ Repair/Replace Window Screens
○ Check Basement for Water Leaks
○
○
○
○
○

MAY
○ Clean and Organize Garage
○ Inspect and Clean Outdoor Lighting
○ Check Air Condition
○ Cut Back Shrubs and Trees
○
○
○
○
○

JUNE
○ Apply Fertilizer to Lawn
○ Check and Clear Exhaust Fans
○ Inspect Plumbing for Leaks
○ Clean and Seal Deck
○
○
○
○
○

HOME MAINTENANCE SCHEDULE

JULY
○ Clean Carpets
○ Clean Laundry Room
○ Check Dryer Vent
○ Wash/Clean Curtains
○
○
○
○
○

AUGUST
○ Clean Frig and Freezers
○ Repair Fences And Gates
○ Replace Mulch
○ Clean Woodwork
○
○
○
○
○

SEPTEMBER
○ Install Weather Stripping On Doors And Windows
○ Inspect Furnace
○ Winterize AC
○ Inspect Driveway for Cracks- Repair if Needed
○
○
○
○
○

OCTOBER
○ Turn Off Outdoor Faucets
○ Put Away Hoses
○ Drain Outdoor Pipes
○ Winterize AC
○
○
○
○
○

NOVEMBER
○ Replace Smoke Detector Batteries
○ Clean Gutters
○ Clean Grill and Outdoor Kitchen
○ Put Away Patio Furniture
○
○
○
○
○

DECEMBER
○ Inspect Attic Insulation
○ Insulate Hot Water Heater
○ Check CO2 Monitor
○ Inspect Appliance Hoses
○
○
○
○
○

MAINTENANCE CONTACTS

COMPANY		CONTACT PERSON	
EMAIL		PHONE	
SERVICE PROVIDED			

COMPANY		CONTACT PERSON	
EMAIL		PHONE	
SERVICE PROVIDED			

COMPANY		CONTACT PERSON	
EMAIL		PHONE	
SERVICE PROVIDED			

COMPANY		CONTACT PERSON	
EMAIL		PHONE	
SERVICE PROVIDED			

COMPANY		CONTACT PERSON	
EMAIL		PHONE	
SERVICE PROVIDED			

COMPANY		CONTACT PERSON	
EMAIL		PHONE	
SERVICE PROVIDED			

COMPANY		CONTACT PERSON	
EMAIL		PHONE	
SERVICE PROVIDED			

COMPANY		CONTACT PERSON	
EMAIL		PHONE	
SERVICE PROVIDED			

COMPANY		CONTACT PERSON	
EMAIL		PHONE	
SERVICE PROVIDED			

MAINTENANCE CONTACTS

COMPANY		CONTACT PERSON	
EMAIL		PHONE	
SERVICE PROVIDED			

COMPANY		CONTACT PERSON	
EMAIL		PHONE	
SERVICE PROVIDED			

COMPANY		CONTACT PERSON	
EMAIL		PHONE	
SERVICE PROVIDED			

COMPANY		CONTACT PERSON	
EMAIL		PHONE	
SERVICE PROVIDED			

COMPANY		CONTACT PERSON	
EMAIL		PHONE	
SERVICE PROVIDED			

COMPANY		CONTACT PERSON	
EMAIL		PHONE	
SERVICE PROVIDED			

COMPANY		CONTACT PERSON	
EMAIL		PHONE	
SERVICE PROVIDED			

COMPANY		CONTACT PERSON	
EMAIL		PHONE	
SERVICE PROVIDED			

COMPANY		CONTACT PERSON	
EMAIL		PHONE	
SERVICE PROVIDED			

MAINTENANCE CONTACTS

COMPANY		CONTACT PERSON	
EMAIL		PHONE	
SERVICE PROVIDED			

COMPANY		CONTACT PERSON	
EMAIL		PHONE	
SERVICE PROVIDED			

COMPANY		CONTACT PERSON	
EMAIL		PHONE	
SERVICE PROVIDED			

COMPANY		CONTACT PERSON	
EMAIL		PHONE	
SERVICE PROVIDED			

COMPANY		CONTACT PERSON	
EMAIL		PHONE	
SERVICE PROVIDED			

COMPANY		CONTACT PERSON	
EMAIL		PHONE	
SERVICE PROVIDED			

COMPANY		CONTACT PERSON	
EMAIL		PHONE	
SERVICE PROVIDED			

COMPANY		CONTACT PERSON	
EMAIL		PHONE	
SERVICE PROVIDED			

COMPANY		CONTACT PERSON	
EMAIL		PHONE	
SERVICE PROVIDED			

JANUARY MAINTENANCE LOG

DATE	SYSTEM / APPLIANCE	SERVICE	COST	DATE COMPLETED	NOTES

JANUARY MAINTENANCE RECEIPTS

SERVICE	COMPANY	DATE COMPLETED	COST

FEBRUARY MAINTENANCE LOG

DATE	SYSTEM / APPLIANCE	SERVICE	COST	DATE COMPLETED	NOTES

FEBRUARY MAINTENANCE RECEIPTS

SERVICE	COMPANY	DATE COMPLETED	COST

MARCH MAINTENANCE LOG

DATE	SYSTEM / APPLIANCE	SERVICE	COST	DATE COMPLETED	NOTES

MARCH MAINTENANCE RECEIPTS

SERVICE	COMPANY	DATE COMPLETED	COST

APRIL MAINTENANCE LOG

DATE	SYSTEM / APPLIANCE	SERVICE	COST	DATE COMPLETED	NOTES

APRIL MAINTENANCE RECEIPTS

SERVICE	COMPANY	DATE COMPLETED	COST

MAY MAINTENANCE LOG

DATE	SYSTEM / APPLIANCE	SERVICE	COST	DATE COMPLETED	NOTES

MAY MAINTENANCE RECEIPTS

SERVICE	COMPANY	DATE COMPLETED	COST

JUNE MAINTENANCE LOG

DATE	SYSTEM / APPLIANCE	SERVICE	COST	DATE COMPLETED	NOTES

JUNE MAINTENANCE RECEIPTS

SERVICE	COMPANY	DATE COMPLETED	COST

JULY MAINTENANCE LOG

DATE	SYSTEM / APPLIANCE	SERVICE	COST	DATE COMPLETED	NOTES

JULY MAINTENANCE RECEIPTS

SERVICE	COMPANY	DATE COMPLETED	COST

AUGUST MAINTENANCE LOG

DATE	SYSTEM / APPLIANCE	SERVICE	COST	DATE COMPLETED	NOTES

AUGUST MAINTENANCE RECEIPTS

SERVICE	COMPANY	DATE COMPLETED	COST

SEPTEMBER MAINTENANCE LOG

DATE	SYSTEM / APPLIANCE	SERVICE	COST	DATE COMPLETED	NOTES

SEPTEMBER MAINTENANCE RECEIPTS

SERVICE	COMPANY	DATE COMPLETED	COST

OCTOBER MAINTENANCE LOG

DATE	SYSTEM / APPLIANCE	SERVICE	COST	DATE COMPLETED	NOTES

OCTOBER MAINTENANCE RECEIPTS

SERVICE	COMPANY	DATE COMPLETED	COST

NOVEMBER MAINTENANCE LOG

DATE	SYSTEM / APPLIANCE	SERVICE	COST	DATE COMPLETED	NOTES

NOVEMBER MAINTENANCE RECEIPTS

SERVICE	COMPANY	DATE COMPLETED	COST

DECEMBER MAINTENANCE LOG

DATE	SYSTEM / APPLIANCE	SERVICE	COST	DATE COMPLETED	NOTES

DECEMBER MAINTENANCE RECEIPTS

SERVICE	COMPANY	DATE COMPLETED	COST

PROJECT PLANNER

PROJECT	

PROJECT DESCRIPTION

COMPLETION DATE

TOTAL BUDGET

PROJECT NOTES

MATERIALS LIST	EXPECTED COST	ACTUAL COST

PROFESSIONAL SERVICES	EXPECTED COST	ACTUAL COST
		TOTAL COST

PROJECT PLANNER

PROJECT	

PROJECT DESCRIPTION
COMPLETION DATE
TOTAL BUDGET
PROJECT NOTES

MATERIALS LIST	EXPECTED COST	ACTUAL COST

PROFESSIONAL SERVICES	EXPECTED COST	ACTUAL COST
		TOTAL COST

PROJECT PLANNER

PROJECT	

PROJECT DESCRIPTION

COMPLETION DATE

TOTAL BUDGET

PROJECT NOTES

MATERIALS LIST	EXPECTED COST	ACTUAL COST

PROFESSIONAL SERVICES	EXPECTED COST	ACTUAL COST
		TOTAL COST

PROJECT PLANNER

PROJECT	

PROJECT DESCRIPTION
COMPLETION DATE
TOTAL BUDGET
PROJECT NOTES

MATERIALS LIST	EXPECTED COST	ACTUAL COST

PROFESSIONAL SERVICES	EXPECTED COST	ACTUAL COST
		TOTAL COST

PROJECT PLANNER

PROJECT	

PROJECT DESCRIPTION

COMPLETION DATE

TOTAL BUDGET

PROJECT NOTES

MATERIALS LIST	EXPECTED COST	ACTUAL COST

PROFESSIONAL SERVICES	EXPECTED COST	ACTUAL COST
		TOTAL COST

PROJECT PLANNER

PROJECT	

PROJECT DESCRIPTION
COMPLETION DATE
TOTAL BUDGET
PROJECT NOTES

MATERIALS LIST	EXPECTED COST	ACTUAL COST

PROFESSIONAL SERVICES	EXPECTED COST	ACTUAL COST
		TOTAL COST

PROJECT PLANNER

PROJECT	

PROJECT DESCRIPTION

COMPLETION DATE

TOTAL BUDGET

PROJECT NOTES

MATERIALS LIST	EXPECTED COST	ACTUAL COST

PROFESSIONAL SERVICES	EXPECTED COST	ACTUAL COST
		TOTAL COST

PROJECT PLANNER

PROJECT	

PROJECT DESCRIPTION

COMPLETION DATE

TOTAL BUDGET

PROJECT NOTES

MATERIALS LIST	EXPECTED COST	ACTUAL COST

PROFESSIONAL SERVICES	EXPECTED COST	ACTUAL COST
		TOTAL COST

PROJECT PLANNER

PROJECT	

PROJECT DESCRIPTION
COMPLETION DATE
TOTAL BUDGET
PROJECT NOTES

MATERIALS LIST	EXPECTED COST	ACTUAL COST

PROFESSIONAL SERVICES	EXPECTED COST	ACTUAL COST
		TOTAL COST

PROJECT PLANNER

PROJECT	

PROJECT DESCRIPTION

COMPLETION DATE

TOTAL BUDGET

PROJECT NOTES

MATERIALS LIST	EXPECTED COST	ACTUAL COST

PROFESSIONAL SERVICES	EXPECTED COST	ACTUAL COST
		TOTAL COST

PROJECT PLANNER

PROJECT	

PROJECT DESCRIPTION

COMPLETION DATE

TOTAL BUDGET

PROJECT NOTES

MATERIALS LIST	EXPECTED COST	ACTUAL COST

PROFESSIONAL SERVICES	EXPECTED COST	ACTUAL COST
		TOTAL COST

PROJECT PLANNER

PROJECT	

PROJECT DESCRIPTION

COMPLETION DATE

TOTAL BUDGET

PROJECT NOTES

MATERIALS LIST	EXPECTED COST	ACTUAL COST

PROFESSIONAL SERVICES	EXPECTED COST	ACTUAL COST
		TOTAL COST

PROJECT PLANNER

PROJECT	

PROJECT DESCRIPTION

COMPLETION DATE

TOTAL BUDGET

PROJECT NOTES

MATERIALS LIST	EXPECTED COST	ACTUAL COST

PROFESSIONAL SERVICES	EXPECTED COST	ACTUAL COST
		TOTAL COST

PROJECT PLANNER

PROJECT	

PROJECT DESCRIPTION
COMPLETION DATE
TOTAL BUDGET
PROJECT NOTES

MATERIALS LIST	EXPECTED COST	ACTUAL COST

PROFESSIONAL SERVICES	EXPECTED COST	ACTUAL COST
		TOTAL COST

PROJECT PLANNER

PROJECT	

PROJECT DESCRIPTION
COMPLETION DATE
TOTAL BUDGET
PROJECT NOTES

MATERIALS LIST	EXPECTED COST	ACTUAL COST

PROFESSIONAL SERVICES	EXPECTED COST	ACTUAL COST
		TOTAL COST

PROJECT PLANNER

PROJECT	

PROJECT DESCRIPTION

COMPLETION DATE

TOTAL BUDGET

PROJECT NOTES

MATERIALS LIST	EXPECTED COST	ACTUAL COST

PROFESSIONAL SERVICES	EXPECTED COST	ACTUAL COST
		TOTAL COST

PROJECT PLANNER

PROJECT	

PROJECT DESCRIPTION

COMPLETION DATE

TOTAL BUDGET

PROJECT NOTES

MATERIALS LIST	EXPECTED COST	ACTUAL COST

PROFESSIONAL SERVICES	EXPECTED COST	ACTUAL COST
		TOTAL COST

PROJECT PLANNER

PROJECT	

PROJECT DESCRIPTION

COMPLETION DATE

TOTAL BUDGET

PROJECT NOTES

MATERIALS LIST	EXPECTED COST	ACTUAL COST

PROFESSIONAL SERVICES	EXPECTED COST	ACTUAL COST
		TOTAL COST

PROJECT PLANNER

PROJECT	

PROJECT DESCRIPTION

COMPLETION DATE

TOTAL BUDGET

PROJECT NOTES

MATERIALS LIST	EXPECTED COST	ACTUAL COST

PROFESSIONAL SERVICES	EXPECTED COST	ACTUAL COST
		TOTAL COST

PROJECT PLANNER

PROJECT	

PROJECT DESCRIPTION

COMPLETION DATE

TOTAL BUDGET

PROJECT NOTES

MATERIALS LIST	EXPECTED COST	ACTUAL COST

PROFESSIONAL SERVICES	EXPECTED COST	ACTUAL COST
		TOTAL COST

PROJECT PLANNER

PROJECT	

PROJECT DESCRIPTION
COMPLETION DATE
TOTAL BUDGET
PROJECT NOTES

MATERIALS LIST	EXPECTED COST	ACTUAL COST

PROFESSIONAL SERVICES	EXPECTED COST	ACTUAL COST
		TOTAL COST

HOME IMPROVEMENT PROJECT PLANNER

PROJECT		DATE	

NOTES / RESOURCES

BUDGET

MATERIALS

TIMELINE

STEPS / TO DO

HOME IMPROVEMENT PROJECT PLANNER

PROJECT		DATE	

NOTES / RESOURCES

BUDGET

MATERIALS

TIMELINE

STEPS / TO DO

HOME IMPROVEMENT PROJECT PLANNER

PROJECT		DATE	

NOTES / RESOURCES

BUDGET

MATERIALS

TIMELINE

STEPS / TO DO

HOME IMPROVEMENT PROJECT PLANNER

PROJECT		DATE	

NOTES / RESOURCES

BUDGET

MATERIALS

TIMELINE

STEPS / TO DO

HOME IMPROVEMENT PROJECT PLANNER

PROJECT		DATE	

NOTES / RESOURCES

BUDGET

MATERIALS

TIMELINE

STEPS / TO DO

HOME IMPROVEMENT PROJECT PLANNER

PROJECT		DATE	

NOTES / RESOURCES

BUDGET

MATERIALS

TIMELINE

STEPS / TO DO

HOME IMPROVEMENT PROJECT PLANNER

PROJECT		DATE	

NOTES / RESOURCES

BUDGET

MATERIALS

TIMELINE

STEPS / TO DO

HOME IMPROVEMENT PROJECT PLANNER

PROJECT		DATE	

NOTES / RESOURCES

BUDGET

MATERIALS

TIMELINE

STEPS / TO DO

HOME IMPROVEMENT PROJECT PLANNER

PROJECT		DATE	

NOTES / RESOURCES

BUDGET

MATERIALS

TIMELINE

STEPS / TO DO

HOME IMPROVEMENT PROJECT PLANNER

PROJECT		DATE	

NOTES / RESOURCES

BUDGET

MATERIALS

TIMELINE

STEPS / TO DO

HOME IMPROVEMENT PROJECT PLANNER

PROJECT		DATE	

NOTES / RESOURCES

BUDGET

MATERIALS

TIMELINE

STEPS / TO DO

HOME IMPROVEMENT PROJECT PLANNER

PROJECT		DATE	

NOTES / RESOURCES

BUDGET

MATERIALS

TIMELINE

STEPS / TO DO

HOME IMPROVEMENT PROJECT PLANNER

PROJECT		DATE	

NOTES / RESOURCES

BUDGET

MATERIALS

TIMELINE

STEPS / TO DO

HOME IMPROVEMENT PROJECT PLANNER

PROJECT		DATE	

NOTES / RESOURCES

BUDGET

MATERIALS

TIMELINE

STEPS / TO DO

HOME IMPROVEMENT PROJECT PLANNER

PROJECT		DATE	

NOTES / RESOURCES

BUDGET

MATERIALS

TIMELINE

STEPS / TO DO

HOME IMPROVEMENT PROJECT PLANNER

PROJECT		DATE	

NOTES / RESOURCES

BUDGET

MATERIALS

TIMELINE

STEPS / TO DO

HOME IMPROVEMENT PROJECT PLANNER

PROJECT		DATE	

NOTES / RESOURCES

BUDGET

MATERIALS

TIMELINE

STEPS / TO DO

HOME IMPROVEMENT PROJECT PLANNER

PROJECT		DATE	

NOTES / RESOURCES

BUDGET

MATERIALS

TIMELINE

STEPS / TO DO

HOME IMPROVEMENT PROJECT PLANNER

PROJECT		DATE	

NOTES / RESOURCES

BUDGET

MATERIALS

TIMELINE

STEPS / TO DO

HOME IMPROVEMENT PROJECT PLANNER

PROJECT		DATE	

NOTES / RESOURCES

BUDGET

MATERIALS

TIMELINE

STEPS / TO DO

HOME IMPROVEMENT PROJECT PLANNER

PROJECT		DATE	

NOTES / RESOURCES

BUDGET

MATERIALS

TIMELINE

STEPS / TO DO

HOME IMPROVEMENT PROJECT PLANNER

PROJECT		DATE	

NOTES / RESOURCES

BUDGET

MATERIALS

TIMELINE

STEPS / TO DO

HOUSEHOLD MANUFACTURERS

PRODUCT	MANUFACTURER	BRAND / MODEL	CONTACT
REFRIGERATOR / FREEZER			
DISHWASHER			
STOVE TOP RANGE			
OVEN			
MICROWAVE			
GARBAGE DISPOSAL			
WASHING MACHINE			
FIREPLACE			
WATER HEATER			
AIR CONDITIONER			
FURNACE			
LAWN MOWER			
WEEDEATER			
FENCE			
SECURITY SYSTEM			
GARAGE DOOR			

HOUSEHOLD MANUFACTURERS

PRODUCT	MANUFACTURER	BRAND / MODEL	CONTACT

HOUSEHOLD WARRANTIES

PRODUCT	BRAND / MODEL	VALID DATES	OVERVIEW

HOUSEHOLD WARRANTIES

PRODUCT	BRAND / MODEL	VALID DATES	OVERVIEW

HOUSEHOLD WARRANTIES

PRODUCT	BRAND / MODEL	VALID DATES	OVERVIEW

WARRANTY LOG

ITEM		PURCHASED DATE	
FROM		COST	
EXPIRATION DATE		WARRANTY CONTACT	

ITEM		PURCHASED DATE	
FROM		COST	
EXPIRATION DATE		WARRANTY CONTACT	

ITEM		PURCHASED DATE	
FROM		COST	
EXPIRATION DATE		WARRANTY CONTACT	

ITEM		PURCHASED DATE	
FROM		COST	
EXPIRATION DATE		WARRANTY CONTACT	

ITEM		PURCHASED DATE	
FROM		COST	
EXPIRATION DATE		WARRANTY CONTACT	

ITEM		PURCHASED DATE	
FROM		COST	
EXPIRATION DATE		WARRANTY CONTACT	

ITEM		PURCHASED DATE	
FROM		COST	
EXPIRATION DATE		WARRANTY CONTACT	

ITEM		PURCHASED DATE	
FROM		COST	
EXPIRATION DATE		WARRANTY CONTACT	

ITEM		PURCHASED DATE	
FROM		COST	
EXPIRATION DATE		WARRANTY CONTACT	

WARRANTY LOG

ITEM		PURCHASED DATE	
FROM		COST	
EXPIRATION DATE		WARRANTY CONTACT	

ITEM		PURCHASED DATE	
FROM		COST	
EXPIRATION DATE		WARRANTY CONTACT	

ITEM		PURCHASED DATE	
FROM		COST	
EXPIRATION DATE		WARRANTY CONTACT	

ITEM		PURCHASED DATE	
FROM		COST	
EXPIRATION DATE		WARRANTY CONTACT	

ITEM		PURCHASED DATE	
FROM		COST	
EXPIRATION DATE		WARRANTY CONTACT	

ITEM		PURCHASED DATE	
FROM		COST	
EXPIRATION DATE		WARRANTY CONTACT	

ITEM		PURCHASED DATE	
FROM		COST	
EXPIRATION DATE		WARRANTY CONTACT	

ITEM		PURCHASED DATE	
FROM		COST	
EXPIRATION DATE		WARRANTY CONTACT	

ITEM		PURCHASED DATE	
FROM		COST	
EXPIRATION DATE		WARRANTY CONTACT	

WARRANTY LOG

ITEM		PURCHASED DATE	
FROM		COST	
EXPIRATION DATE		WARRANTY CONTACT	

ITEM		PURCHASED DATE	
FROM		COST	
EXPIRATION DATE		WARRANTY CONTACT	

ITEM		PURCHASED DATE	
FROM		COST	
EXPIRATION DATE		WARRANTY CONTACT	

ITEM		PURCHASED DATE	
FROM		COST	
EXPIRATION DATE		WARRANTY CONTACT	

ITEM		PURCHASED DATE	
FROM		COST	
EXPIRATION DATE		WARRANTY CONTACT	

ITEM		PURCHASED DATE	
FROM		COST	
EXPIRATION DATE		WARRANTY CONTACT	

ITEM		PURCHASED DATE	
FROM		COST	
EXPIRATION DATE		WARRANTY CONTACT	

ITEM		PURCHASED DATE	
FROM		COST	
EXPIRATION DATE		WARRANTY CONTACT	

ITEM		PURCHASED DATE	
FROM		COST	
EXPIRATION DATE		WARRANTY CONTACT	

WARRANTY LOG

ITEM		PURCHASED DATE	
FROM		COST	
EXPIRATION DATE		WARRANTY CONTACT	

ITEM		PURCHASED DATE	
FROM		COST	
EXPIRATION DATE		WARRANTY CONTACT	

ITEM		PURCHASED DATE	
FROM		COST	
EXPIRATION DATE		WARRANTY CONTACT	

ITEM		PURCHASED DATE	
FROM		COST	
EXPIRATION DATE		WARRANTY CONTACT	

ITEM		PURCHASED DATE	
FROM		COST	
EXPIRATION DATE		WARRANTY CONTACT	

ITEM		PURCHASED DATE	
FROM		COST	
EXPIRATION DATE		WARRANTY CONTACT	

ITEM		PURCHASED DATE	
FROM		COST	
EXPIRATION DATE		WARRANTY CONTACT	

ITEM		PURCHASED DATE	
FROM		COST	
EXPIRATION DATE		WARRANTY CONTACT	

ITEM		PURCHASED DATE	
FROM		COST	
EXPIRATION DATE		WARRANTY CONTACT	

Printed in the USA
CPSIA information can be obtained
at www.ICGtesting.com
CBHW061841261123
2146CB00009B/53